Every boy and girl loves
riddles, jokes, and funny poems.
The selected ones in this book are
really super. Kids will find them
hilarious, and many adults will
chuckle as well.

Here is a heritage of fun.

# Riddles, Rhymes, & Jokes

MAURICE GILMAN STONE

Hart Publishing Company, Inc. New York City

# CONTENTS

# Riddles

There are four of them in every city and town. What are they?

*Letters.*

What's the difference between a thief and a church bell?

*One steals from the people and the other peals from the steeple.*

What ten-letter word starts with G-A-S?

*Automobile.*

How does a dog wear more clothes in summer than in winter?

*In winter he wears a coat; in summer, he wears a coat and pants.*

What words may be pronounced quicker and shorter by adding syllables to them?

*Quick and short.*

A duck in front of two ducks; a duck behind two ducks; and a duck between two ducks. How many ducks were there in all?

*Three ducks.*

What pets make sweet music?
    *Trum-pets!*

What could you call an alligator who goes bowling?
    *An alley gator.*

Behind each boy is a girl. Behind each girl is a boy. Now, what is the smallest number of pupils that can be arranged in that manner?
    *One boy and one girl—back to back.*

From a word with five letters, take two and leave one.
    *Al-one.*

Why is the letter D like a sailor?
    *Because it follows the C.*

What's colorless, wet, and turns dark when you wash it?
    *Water.*

What is the difference between here and there?
    *The letter T.*

What is that which no man wants, yet no man would wish to lose?

*A bald head.*

What is that which goes with a train, comes with a train, is no use to the train, yet the train cannot go without it?

*Noise.*

Which word is always pronounced wrong?

*Wrong.*

Why are you tired on April Fool's Day?

*Because you have just had a March of thirty-one days.*

What international catastrophe would be caused by a waiter who dropped a platter on Thanksgiving?

*It would be the downfall of Turkey, the overthrow of Greece, and the destruction of China.*

Why is an archaeologist always unsuccessful?

*Because his career lies in ruins.*

What is everyone in the world doing at the same time?

*Growing older.*

How does a tuna fish differ from a piano?

*You can't tune a fish.*

What is white when it goes up, but yellow and white when it comes down?

*An egg.*

What man shaves more than fifteen times a day?

*A barber.*

What bus crossed the Atlantic?

*Columbus.*

What is the difference between the North Pole and the South Pole?
*All the difference in the world!*

*Which side of an apple pie is the left side?*
*The part that isn't eaten.*

What has more lives than a cat?
*The frog; he croaks every night.*

If a little lamb is a lambkin, what is a little sleep?
*A napkin.*

What is most useful when it's used up?
*An umbrella.*

Which is proper to say—3 plus 5 is 7, or 3 plus 5 are 7?
*Neither. 3 plus 5 are 8.*

What is the difference between a conductor and a teacher?
*A conductor minds the train and a teacher trains the mind.*

At what time of day was Adam created?
*A little before Eve.*

What pine has the longest and the sharpest needles?
*The porcupine!*

When is a baseball catcher like a farmer?
*When he chases a foul.*

What question can never be answered by "Yes"?
*"Are you asleep?"*

What do you find only once in room, but twice in every corner?
*The letter R.*

Who was the fastest runner in the world?
*Adam. He was the first in the human race.*

What trees are left behind after a fire?
*Ashes.*

What is more useful after it's broken?
*An egg.*

How do we know that a dentist is unhappy?
*Because he looks down in the mouth.*

Why is the letter R necessary for friendship?
*Because without it, your friends would be fiends.*

Why don't we ever have a minute to ourselves?
*Because the minutes aren't hours.*

When is a farmer cruel to his corn?
*At harvest time, when he must pull its ears.*

What has five eyes and goes south?
*The Mississippi River.*

Why did the corn stalk hear so much?
*Because it was all ears.*

What was the largest island before Australia was
discovered?
   *Australia.*

*What is the difference between an old dime and a new
penny?*
   *Nine cents.*

What three words (which read the same backwards and
forwards) might Adam have used to introduce himself to
Eve?
   *"Madam, I'm Adam."*

Why is it wrong to whisper?
   *Because it is not aloud.*

If eight sparrows are on a roof and you shoot one, how
many remain?
   *One. The one you shot. The rest fly away.*

What is the best material for kites?
   *Flypaper.*

One morning a boy couldn't find his trousers, so what did he
do?
   *He raced around the room until he was breathing
   in short pants.*

What goes through a door, but never goes in or comes out?
   *A keyhole.*

What is the difference between a dancer and a duck?
   *One goes quick on her legs, the other goes "quack"
   on her eggs.*

What is that which never uses its teeth for eating purposes?
   *A comb.*

What is the hardest thing about learning to ride a bicycle?
   *The ground!*

What kind of a house weighs the least?
   *A lighthouse.*

What's the use of snow shovel?
   *Snow use.*

Why is the letter D like a wedding ring?
   *Because we could not have wed without it.*

What can always be found between here and there?
   *And.*

What is the hottest letter?
   *B, because it makes oil boil.*

When is a store like a boat?
   *When it has sales.*

Why is it hard for a leopard to hide?
   *Because, no matter where it goes, it's always spotted.*

What kind of clothing lasts the longest?
   *Underwear—because it's never worn out.*

What makes you sick if you take away the first letter?
    *Music.*

Why should your mother never put the letter M into the
freezer?
    *Because it changes ice into mice.*

What is the coldest row in a theater?
    *Z row (zero).*

What animal has the head of a cat, the tail of a cat, the
ways of a cat, and yet isn't a cat?
    *A kitten.*

Why is a baby the least important member of a family?
    *Because it doesn't count.*

When are you like the letter B?
    *When you are in bed.*

Why is an empty purse always the same?
    *Because there is never any change in it.*

Why is a policeman the strongest man in the world?
    *Because he can hold up a whole line of cars, with one
    hand.*

What goes under the water, over the water, yet never touches the water?

*A woman crossing the bridge with a pail of water on her head.*

Where did Noah strike the first nail on the ark?

*On the head.*

Why aren't baseball players going to use bats any longer?

*Because the bats are long enough now.*

How can you add ten to ten and still have ten?

*Put on gloves.*

Why wasn't the man seriously hurt when he fell off the cliff?

*Because he had on his light fall overcoat.*

What did the big chimney say to the little chimney?

*"You're not big enough to smoke."*

What smells the most in a zoo?

*Your nose.*

Why is a star like a window in the roof?

*Because it's a skylight.*

15

What coat has no sleeves?
*A coat of paint.*

What runs around the yard but never budges an inch?
*A fence.*

Schenectady is a city in New York. How do you spell it?
*I-T.*

What is the difference between a busy typist and 16 ounces of flour?
*One pounds away; the other weighs a pound.*

To what question must you positively answer yes?
*What does Y-E-S spell?*

What animal do you look like when you go in swimming?
*A little bear.*

Why is a lollipop like a horse?
*Because the more you lick it the faster it goes.*

What has three feet but cannot walk?
*A yard.*

What two things that Adam never had did he leave to his children?
*Parents.*

Why is a room full of married couples like an empty room?
*Because there isn't a single person in it.*

When the clock strikes 13 what time is it?
*Time to get it fixed.*

Why are pianos like good people?
*Because they are grand, upright, and square.*

What money would a gatekeeper collect at an animal fair?

*A (s)cent from a skunk, a greenback from a frog, a bill from a duck, and quarters from a cow.*

When do 2 and 2 make more than 4?

*When they make 22.*

What is the difference between a home, a sigh and a donkey?

*A home is so dear, a sigh is oh dear, and a donkey is you, dear.*

Which travels faster, heat or cold?

*Heat, because you can easily catch cold.*

What is the difference between a jeweler and a jailer?

*One sells watches and the other watches cells.*

What word of seven letters will have six left after you take away four?

*Sixteen.*

What are the largest ants in the world?

*Giants.*

To whom do men always take their hats off?

*The barber.*

Why are flowers lazy?
*Because you'll always find them in beds.*

What flower grows between the nose and the chin?
*Tulips.*

Why is 2 and 2 make 5 like a left foot?
*Because it isn't right.*

What has a mouth and a fork but never eats?
*A river.*

What bird lifts the heaviest weights?
*The crane.*

What is the best thing to put into cakes?
*Your teeth!*

What is the difference between a postage stamp and a woman?
*One is a mail fee and the other is a female.*

What is that which goes up-hill and all over everywhere, yet never moves?
*A road.*

What goes on and on and has an eye in the middle?
*Onion.*

What kind of cat do you always find in the library?
*A catalogue.*

If athletes get athlete's foot, what do astronauts get?
*Missile toe.*

What is as old as the mountains?
*The valleys between them.*

Why is a baseball team like a pancake?
*Because its success depends on the batter.*

What always has an eye open, but never sees?
*A needle.*

What state is round at both ends and high in the middle?
*O-hi-o.*

Why do snowflakes dance about?
*They are getting ready for the snowball.*

Why did the man forget all about the tooth that the dentist pulled?
*Because it went right out of his head.*

Why is a hen sitting on a fence like a penny?
*Because she has a head on one side and a tail on the other.*

Why is a dog that rides in an automobile like a covering for the floor?
*It is a car pet.*

What must you add to nine to make it six?
*The letter S. Put down IX—the Roman way of writing 9. Put an S in front of it and it becomes SIX.*

What cannot run although it has three feet?
*A yard.*

What is about three inches tall, nine inches long, four inches wide, and contains a solid foot?
*A shoe.*

What kind of hen lays the longest?
*A dead one.*

What is 9 inches long, and has purple spots and 50 legs?
*I don't know either, but you better pick it off your neck.*

Why should you be careful about telling secrets in the country?
*Because the corn has ears, the potatoes have eyes.
and the beans talk (beanstalk).*

When you lose something why do you always find it in the last place you look?
*Because you stop looking when you find it.*

Why are fishermen so stingy?
*Because their business makes them sell fish (selfish).*

20

Why would a spider make a good ball player?
*Because it is good at catching flies.*

What state doesn't feel so good?
*Ill.*

On which side does a leopard have the most spots?
*On the outside.*

What is the laziest mountain in the world?
*Mount Everest.*

If a carrot and a cabbage ran a race, which would win?
*The cabbage, because it's a head.*

Why shouldn't one trust the ocean completely?
*There's something fishy about it.*

Seven is an odd number. How can it be made even?
*Take away the S.*

How do you keep cool at a ball game?
*Stay near a fan.*

Why is your hand like a hardware store?
*Because it carries nails.*

If a farmer carries a sack of grain and his hired man
carries two sacks, which has to carry the heavier load?
*The farmer—because the grain is heavier than
two sacks.*

Why do bees hum?
*Because they don't know the words.*

What state is a musical note?
*La.*

What ring is best for a telephone?
*Answering.*

Why should bowling alleys be quiet?
*So that one can hear a pin drop!*

What is invisible, yet never out of sight?
*The letter S.*

What is the best day for making pancakes?
*Fri-day.*

You see ten dogs running down the street. What time is it?
*Nine after one.*

How many peas in a pint?
*One P.*

How many soft-boiled eggs can a giant eat on an empty stomach?
*One.  After that, his stomach is no longer empty.*

There is a girl who works in a candy store in Los Angeles. She is five feet tall, her waist measures 36 inches, and she wears a size 9 shoe. What do you think she weighs?
*She weighs candy.*

What can be divided, but no one can see where it was
divided?
    *Water.*

There were sixteen ears of corn in a barrel. Each night a
rabbit came and carried away three ears. How long did it
take the rabbit to empty the barrel?
    *Sixteen nights. One ear of corn and his own two ears
    carried away each night.*

If a man gives fifteen cents to one of his sons, and a dime to
another, what time is it?
    *A quarter to two.*

What is the fruit of history?
    *Dates.*

Why is it bad to write on an empty stomach?
    *It's not so bad, but paper is easier.*

Where did Marco Polo go on his thirty-ninth birthday?
    *Into his fortieth year.*

What is found only in the very center of America and
Australia?
    *The letter R.*

Why is E the most unlucky letter?
*Because it is never in cash, always in debt, and never out of danger.*

Why isn't it safe to keep a clock at the top of the stairs?
*It might run down and strike one.*

When are the roads unpleasant?
*When they are crossroads.*

What is the difference between a king's son, a monkey's mother, a bald head, and an orphan?
*One is an heir apparent, one is a hairy parent, one has no hair apparent, and one has nary a parent.*

What are the strongest days of the week?
*Saturday and Sunday. The rest are week-days.*

How did Little Bo-Peep lose her sheep?
*She had a crook with her.*

If a man dropped shaving cream on the stove, what would he have?
*Foam on the range.*

Where were the first doughnuts fried?
   *In Greece.*

What is the noblest of all dogs?
   *The hot dog because it feeds the hand that bites it.*

What has eight legs, two arms, three heads, and two wings?
   *A man riding a horse and carrying a chicken.*

What has 18 legs and catches flies?
   *A baseball team.*

What animal took the most luggage into the Ark, and what animal took the least?
   *The elephant took his trunk, and the rooster had only a comb.*

What is the last thing you take off before going to bed?
   *Your feet off the floor.*

What do you call a bird that got caught in a lawnmower?
   *Shredded tweet.*

Why is a dog's tail like the heart of a tree?
   *Because it's farthest from the bark.*

Why did the silly man buy chewing gum on the train?
   *Because he heard the engine saying, "Choo-choo!"*

What tune is music to anybody's ear?
   *For-tune.*

What is too much for one, just right for two, but nothing at all for three?
   *A secret.*

What animal drops from the clouds?
   *The rein, deer.*

Why is a pig in the parlor like a house on fire?
*The sooner both are put out, the better.*

What fruit is on a dime?
*A date.*

What kind of cans may be found on the floor of the United States Congress?
*Republicans.*

What are the smartest letters in the alphabet?
*The Y's (wise).*

Who was the greatest actor in the Bible?
*Samson. He brought down the house.*

Why is a pencil like a riddle?
*It is no good without a point.*

Why does a hen lay eggs?
*Because if she dropped them they would break.*

What is the chief cause of divorce?
*Marriage.*

Why is the letter d like a bad boy?
*Because it makes ma mad.*

Six legs, two heads, two hands, and a nose,
But uses only four legs as it goes.
*Man on horseback.*

Did you ever hear the story of the new roof?
*It's way over your head.*

Why is a boxer like a candle?
*Because a good blow will put them out.*

What could you call a crying contest?
*A bawl game.*

What animals are in banks?
*Doe and bucks.*

What bird is always seen in June and July?
*A jay (J).*

What is the difference between a fisherman and a dunce?
*One baits his hooks and the other hates his books.*

If all the money in the world were divided equally among all
the people in the world, what would each one get?
*An equal share.*

How many cubic feet of earth can you take out of a hole
that is three feet square and three feet deep?
*None. It has all been taken out.*

What's in water that puts out fires?
*A fire boat.*

What is the difference between a bottle of medicine and a
bad boy?
*One is well shaken before taken, and the other should
be taken and well shaken.*

What state is a father?
*Pa.*

What can you see in winter that you can't see in summer?
*Your breath.*

What is the best way to start a fire with two sticks?
*Make sure one of them is a match.*

What is it that dances in the yard after it is dead?
*A fallen leaf.*

Why should you never try to sweep out a room?
*Because it's too big a job. Just sweep out the dirt and leave the room there.*

Who can raise things without lifting them?
*A farmer.*

What bird helps us eat?
*The swallow.*

What is bought by the yard but worn by the foot?
*A rug.*

Four men fell into the water, but only three of them got their hair wet. Why?
*One of them was bald-headed.*

Why is the sun like a good loaf of bread?
*Because it's light when it rises!*

Where does Friday come before Thursday?
*In the dictionary.*

How can you say in two letters that you are twice the size of your friend?
*I W*

Why is the letter A like twelve o'clock?
*Because it comes in the middle of day.*

What dog is also a poet?
*A dachshund, because he is a Longfellow.*

What is above a general?
*His hat.*

Which city behaves oddly?
*Eccentricity.*

Why is the letter F like Paris?
*Because it is the capital of France.*

What did Noah say when the animals started climbing into the Ark?
*"Now I herd everything."*

When is a stew like a golden ring?
*When it has 18 carrots (carats).*

What vegetable would you find in a crowded bus?
*Squash.*

# Limericks

There was an old man of Blackheath
Who sat on his set of false teeth;
    He cried, with a start,
    "Oh, Lord bless my heart!
I've bitten myself underneath!"

There was a young lady named Perkins
Who just simply doted on gherkins.
    In spite of advice,
    She ate so much spice,
That she pickled her internal workin's!

A painter, who lived in Great Britain,
Interrupted two girls with their knittin',
   He said, with a sigh,
   "That park bench—well I
Just painted it, right where you're sittin!"

There was a young man named Paul
Who went to a fancy dress ball;
   He thought he would risk it
   And go as a biscuit—
But a dog ate him up in the hall!

There's a young man who lives in Belsize
Who thinks he is clever and wise;
   Why, what do you think?
   He saves gallons of ink
By simply not dotting his i's!

There was a young man of Fort Worth
Who was born on the day of his birth;
    He was married, some say,
    On his wife's wedding day,
And he died when he quitted the earth!

There was a young man from Podunk
Who once tried to capture a skunk.
    The skunk got away,
    And that poor man today
Has his clothes camphored up in a trunk!

A silly young man from the Clyde
In a funeral carriage was spied;
    When asked, "Who is dead?"
    He snickered and said,
"I don't know—I just came for the ride."

There was a young person named Willy
Whose actions were what you'd call silly;
    He went to a ball,
    Dressed in nothing at all,
Pretending to represent Chile!

There was a young man of Devizes,
Whose ears were of different sizes;
    The one that was small
    Was of no use at all,
But the other won several prizes!

There was a young lady in No. Dak.
Who photoed a bear with a kodak.
    The button she pressed—
    The bear did the rest;
The lady stopped running in So. Dak.!

A cheerful old bear at the zoo
Could always find something to do.
    When it bored him, you know,
    To walk to and fro,
He reversed it—and walked fro and to!

There was a young lady of Crete
Who was so exceedingly neat—
    When she got out of bed
    She stood on her head
To make sure of not soiling her feet!

There was an old fellow named Green,
Who grew so abnormally lean,
    And flat, and compressed,
    That his back touched his chest,
And sideways he couldn't be seen.

There was a young fellow named Hall
Who fell in the spring in the fall;
    'Twould have been a sad thing
    If he died in the spring.
But he didn't—he died in the fall!

A tutor who tooted a flute
Tried to teach two young tooters to toot,
    Said the two to the tutor,
    Is it harder to toot, or
To tutor two tooters to toot?


A flea and a fly in a flue
Were imprisoned, so what could they do?
    Said the fly, "Let us flee!"
    Said the flea, "Let us fly!"
So they flew through a flaw in the flue!

Susanna, a sweet little Miss,
Declared roller skating was bliss,
    But she knew not her fate,
    For a wheel off her skate
Made her end up something like this!

A fussy old widow named Pease
Thought her home was infested with fleas;
    So she used gasoline,
    And her form was last seen
Sailing over the tops of the trees!


There was a young fellow named Wier
Who hadn't an atom of fear.
    He indulged a desire
    To touch a live wire.
(Most any last line will do here!)

An epicure dining at Crewe
Found quite a large mouse in the stew;
    Said the waiter, "Don't shout
    And wave it about
Or the rest will be wanting one too!"


I wish that my room had a floor.
I don't so much care for a floor,
    But this walking around
    Without touching the ground
Is getting to be quite a bore!

There was a young lady named Maud,
A very deceptive young fraud;
      She never was able
      To eat at the table,
But out in the pantry—*O Lord!*


There was a young lady said, "Why
Can't I look in my ear with my eye?
      If I put my mind to it,
      I'm sure I can do it—
You never can tell till you try!"

There was an old gent quite weird—
He shrieked, "'Tis just as I feared!
      Two owls and a hen,
      Four larks and a wren
Have all built their nests in my beard!"

# Jokes

STU: Do you know my parents?

PRU: No, I don't.

STU: (With his hand extended):   Meet my paw.


TEACHER: It is the duty of every one to make at least one person happy during the week. Have you done so, Bobby?

BOBBY: Yes.

TEACHER: That's nice. What did you do?

BOBBY: I went to see my aunt, and she was happy when I went home!

KEN: My brother was sick and he went to the doctor.

BEN: Is he feeling better now?

KEN: No, he has a broken arm.

BEN: How did he break it?

KEN: Well, the doctor gave him a prescription and told him no matter what happened to follow that prescription. And the prescription blew out of the window.

ALEX:      What would you do if you were in my shoes?
SID:       Polish them!

TEACHER:   What was George Washington noted for?
JAKE:      His memory.
TEACHER:   What makes you think his memory was so great?
JAKE:      They erected a monument to Washington's
           memory.

MISS WHITE:   As we walk out-of-doors on a cold
              winter's morning and look about us, what do we
              see on every hand?
PUPIL:        Gloves!

AUNT BETH:   Well, Jason, how do you like school?
JASON:       Closed!

ELLEN:       He always calls his wife "Fair Lady."
ELIZABETH:   How romantic! Why does he call her "Fair
             Lady?"
ELLEN:       It's habit—he used to be a bus conductor.

TEACHER:   How many sexes are there?
PUPIL:     Three.
TEACHER:   Three! Can you name them?
PUPIL:     Sure. Male sex, female sex, and insects!

BOBBY:     Teacher, would you scold anyone for something he
           didn't do?
TEACHER:   Of course not. But why, Bobby?
BOBBY:     Well, I didn't do my arithmetic homework.

TEACHER:   Name a deadly poison.
PAUL:      Aviation.
TEACHER:   Don't be foolish.
PAUL:      Well, one drop is almost sure to kill!

TEACHER: What is usually used as a conductor of electricity?
RUTH: Why—er—
TEACHER: Correct, wire. Now tell me, what is the unit of electrical power?
RUTH: The what?
TEACHER: That's absolutely right, the watt.

SARA: Hey, Mom, I got a hundred in school today.
MOM: That's wonderful! What did you get a hundred in?
SARA: In two things. I got forty in reading and sixty in spelling.

TIM: So this is a battle of wits between you and me, eh?
TOM: No—I never attack a man who's unarmed!

GYM TEACHER: Rudy, who gave you that black eye?
RUDY: Nobody gave it to me, sir. I had to fight for it.

STAN: How long was your last cook with you?
JAN: She was never with us; she was against us from the start.

KATE: Whenever I'm in the dumps, I get a new hat.
KITTY: Oh, so that's where you get them!

SWIMMING INSTRUCTOR: And another reason for practicing
your swimming is that swimming
is good for the figure.
ESTHER: Did you ever see a duck?

TEACHER: If you added 600, 27, 96 and 35, and divided that
by 35, what would you get?
DAISY: The wrong answer.

TEACHER: I'm afraid this desk is a little too small for you,
Tim.
TALL TIM: Don't worry about it. I'll add two feet to it when I
sit down.

BOY: May I see you pretty soon?
GIRL: Don't you think I'm pretty now?

LEE: I saw a man run over himself today.
DEE: That's impossible.
LEE: I did. This man drove up to a drugstore and asked
the clerk for a cigar, and the clerk said he did not
have any but they had some across the street. He
asked the clerk to get him one but the clerk said he
couldn't leave the store, so the man ran over
himself.

BILL: Did you hear that Tony got in trouble with Miss
Wilcox today?
GLORIA: No, what happened?
BILL: She asked him to name an invention by which we
can take pictures through walls.
GLORIA: Well?
BILL: He answered, "A window."

LARRY: I have a job in a watch factory.
BARRY: What do you do?
LARRY: Just stand around and make faces!

TEACHER: Judy, what is your favorite flower?
JUDY: Chrysanthemums.
TEACHER: Spell it, Judy.
JUDY: I just changed my mind, Miss Wilson, I like roses much better.


RHODA: Why are you running that steam roller over your field?
FARMER: Well, I figured I'd raise some mashed potatoes this year.

MOVING MAN: Pick up that large trunk. Miss Jenkins doesn't want it there.
ASSISTANT: How do you know? Where is Miss Jenkins?
MOVING MAN: She's under the trunk.


CARL: Did you hear what happened to Toby when his bike ran into a brick wall?
CHRIS: Goodness, no. What did happen?
CARL: Toby was knocked speechless and his bike was knocked spokeless.


PETER: Who is bigger? Mrs. Bigger, Mr. Bigger, or the baby?
PAUL: The baby, of course. He's a little Bigger.

TEACHER: What do you call the last teeth we get?
ALEC: False teeth!

GRANDPA: If you're good, I'll give you this nice new penny.
SONNY: Haven't you got a dirty old dollar?

TEACHER: Ted, why does a moth eat holes in rugs?
TED: Maybe it wants to see the floor show.

TEACHER: Name some things that are very dangerous to get near to, and have horns.
NANCY: Automobiles.

TOURIST: Is this a healthy place?
JERRY: It sure is! When I came here I couldn't utter a word. I had scarcely a hair on my head. I hadn't the strength to walk across the room. Why, I had to be lifted from my bed.
TOURIST: That is wonderful! How long have you been here?
JERRY: I was born here.

MAME: I fell over fifty feet today.
PERRY: You did? Were you hurt?
MAME: No, I was just going through a crowded bus.

VISITOR AT AN ART EXHIBIT: Why did they hang this picture?
FRIEND: Must be because they couldn't find the artist!

JACKIE: My uncle can't decide whether to get a new cow or a bicycle for his farm.
LULU: He'd certainly look silly riding on a cow.
JACKIE: Yeah, but he would look a lot sillier milking a bicycle!

MAY: What do you grow in your garden?
RAY: Tired!

RICHARD: What did one rose say to the other rose?
ROGER: Hi, bud!

MR. CRABBY: Did you scold your little boy for mimicking me?
MRS. SMITH: Yes, I told him not to act like a fool!

INSURANCE MAN: Ever had any accidents?
TEX: No.
INSURANCE MAN: Never had an accident in your life?
TEX: Nope. A snake bit me once, though.
INSURANCE MAN: Well, don't you call that an accident?
TEX: Naw—he bit me on purpose.

CINDY: What are you taking for your cold?
MINDY: Make me an offer!

SOL: Did your watch stop when it dropped to the floor?
IZZIE: Certainly. Did you think it would go straight through?

DONALD: Ma, did you say that the baby's got your eyes and Daddy's nose?
MOTHER: Yes, dear.
DONALD: Well, you'd better watch what he's up to—he's got Grandma's teeth now.

REX: Do you like cauliflower?
TEX: No, sir! And I'm glad I don't; because if I did, I'd eat it—and I hate the stuff.

MOM: Jimmy, there were two pieces of pie in the pantry this morning and now there is only one. How is that?
JIMMY: I don't know. It was so dark I suppose I didn't see the other piece.

44

BOSS: I'm a man of few words. If I beckon with my hand, that means come.

SERVANT: Suits me, sir. I'm a man of few words myself. If I shake my head that means I ain't comin'.

SUE: Do you summer in the country?

STU: No, I simmer in the city!


MADMAN: Get ready to die. I'm going to shoot you.

TOM: Why?

MADMAN: I've always said I'd shoot anyone who looked like me.

TOM: Do I look like you?

MADMAN: Yes.

TOM: Then shoot!


MR. GUSHYGUSH: I'm heartbroken. I've lost my precious little dog Fido.

FRIEND: Why don't you put an advertisement in the newspaper?

MR. GUSHYGUSH: What's the use? Poor Fido can't read.


MR. GREEN: How's your husband getting on, Mrs. Gray?

MRS. GRAY: Well, sometimes he's better, and sometimes he's worse; but from the way he growls and carries on when he's better, I think he's better when he's worse.

LILLY: I'm constantly breaking into song.
BILLY: You wouldn't have to break in, if you had the right key!

MORRIS: This is an ideal spot for a picnic.
BORIS: It must be. Fifty million insects can't be wrong!

MARILYN: I don't like this new photograph. It doesn't do me justice.
PHOTOGRAPHER: It's mercy you want, not justice!

MIKE: Mother, please let me go to the zoo to see the monkeys.
MOTHER: Why, Mike, what an idea! Imagine wanting to go to the zoo to see the monkeys when your Aunt Mitzi is here!

SCIENCE TEACHER: This gas is deadly poison. What steps would you take if it escaped?
WILLIE: Long ones, sir.

DAD: I'm a little worried, son, about your being at the foot of the class.
HUGHIE: Don't worry, Pop. They teach the same stuff at both ends.

MARTIN: Hey, Mom, is that hair tonic in the yellow bottle?

MOTHER: No, Martin, that's glue.

MARTIN: No wonder I couldn't get my hat off when I got to school this morning.

AUNT SUE: Have you learned to spell yet, Willie?

WILLIE: Sure.

AUNT SUE: Let me hear you spell "kitten."

WILLIE: I'm getting too old for kitten. Listen to me spell "cat."

FRED: Did you know that Pete runs to school every day behind the bus to save fifteen cents?

NED: I know how he can save more money every day.

FRED: How?

NED: He can run behind a taxi and save seventy-five cents.

MISS BLACK: John, which letter comes after "A" in the alphabet?

JOHN: All of 'em.

STAN: I went out for end on the football team.

SID: Didn't make it, huh?

STAN: No. I thought I was going to, though. The first day at practice, the coach took one look at me and said, "Oh, brother, this is the end!"

NORMAN: How come you were late today?

ALAN: My bike had a flat tire on the way to school. I must have hit something sharp.

NORMAN: It's your own fault. You know there's a fork in the road on the way to school!

LENNY: Let's play house.

BENNY: Okay—you be the door and I'll slam you!

DEBBY: Mother, today in the school bus a little girl fell off her seat and everyone laughed except me.

MOTHER: That was very kind of you, dear. Who was the little girl?

DEBBY: Me.

CLAUDE: I would like ten cents' worth of bird seed.

CLERK: How many birds do you have, sonny?

CLAUDE: None, but I want to grow some.

BILL: (Eagerly, after running 100 yards): How did I do, coach? Did you take my time?

COACH: (Disgusted): I didn't have to. You took it yourself.

JOE: Say, Moe, what are these holes in the wood?

MOE: They are knotholes.

JOE: Well, if they're not holes, what are they?

TEACHER: Ken, how did you get that horrible swelling on your nose?

KEN: I bent down to smell a brose in my garden.

TEACHER: There's no "b" in rose.

KEN: There was in this one.

MISS WALLACE: Are there any colors you can actually touch?

TIM: Oh yes, Miss Wallace, I've often felt blue.

48

TEACHER: Where are the biggest diamonds found?
JOSEPH: In baseball parks!


KEVIN: Jane Smith would make a good baseball player.
JANE: And why would she make a good baseball player?
KEVIN: A fly got into the bowl when she was making pancakes, and you should have seen how she caught that fly from the batter!

BRENDA: You'd be a fine dancer except for two things.
OLLIE: What?
BRENDA: Your feet!

DAD: Now, Junior, be good while I'm away.
BRUCE: Okay, Pop. I'll be good for a quarter.
DAD: Why, son, when I was your age I was good for nothing.

WOMAN: Please tell me which platform I go to for the train to Boston.
CONDUCTOR: Turn to the left and you'll be right.
WOMAN: Young man, don't be impertinent.
CONDUCTOR: Okay, then turn to the right and you'll be left!

FATHER: Ruthie, why don't you wash your face? I can see what you had for breakfast this morning.

RUTHIE: What was it?

FATHER: Eggs.

RUTHIE: Wrong, Dad! That was yesterday!


MRS. WHITE: Why are you crying, Louie?

LOUIE: Because my brother has a holiday and I haven't.

MRS. WHITE: How come you don't have a holiday?

LOUIE: Because I'm too young to go to school.


BORE (after a three-hour visit): When I hear music I am easily moved.

SORE (eagerly): What do you want me to play for you?

MIKE: I just got a job working down at the Eagle Laundry.

SPIKE: I didn't know they washed eagles!


DICK: I'd like a cup of coffee and a muttered buffin.

BILL: You mean a buffered muttin.

DICK: No, I mean a muffered buttin.

BILL: How about making it a doughnut and milk?

It happened in the school cafeteria:

PEGGY:  Ugh! I hate cream-cheese-and-jelly sandwiches, and every single day I get the same thing for lunch.

POLLY:  Why don't you tell your mother you don't want cream-cheese-and-jelly sandwiches?

PEGGY:  Nope. That wouldn't work. I always make my own sandwiches.


DON:  Al is the first person you learn about when you start in school.

RON:  Al who?

DON:  Alphabet.


SCOTT:  What are the three words most often used by students in school?

GREG:  I don't know.

SCOTT:  Correct.


MILLY:  I've got an idea.

BILLY:  Beginner's luck!


TEACHER:  Tell me the truth now, who did your homework?

JACK:  Father.

TEACHER:  Quite alone?

JACK:  No, I helped him with it!


CLARA:  What's flat at the bottom, pointed at the top, and has ears?

TOM:  I give up.

CLARA:  A mountain.

TOM:  Oh, yeah, what about the ears?

CLARA:  Haven't you ever heard of mountaineers?


JON:  I just saw something running across the floor with no legs.

RON:  Goodness! What was it?

JON:  A glass of spilled milk.

RICHIE: Doctor, when I get well will I be able to play the piano?

DOCTOR: Of course.

RICHIE: That's marvelous. I never played it before!

FATHER: Is there anything you can do better than anyone else?

PETE: Yes, sir, read my own handwriting!

ALF: How do they treat you here?

ANDY: Not very often!

MISS BELL: The fleas we find on domestic animals are small, dark-colored pests.

TEDDY: Gee, Miss Bell, I thought fleas were white.

MISS BELL: Why, Teddy?

TEDDY: I read a poem once that said: "Mary had a little lamb with fleece as white as snow."

PAT: When I sing, people clap their hands.

LUCY: Yeah, clap them over their ears!

MR. JACKSON: I'm quite a near neighbor of yours now—I'm living just across the river.

MR. SOURPUSS: I hope you'll drop in some day![1]

HARRY:   Why is a snake smart?
BARRY:   You can't pull its leg.


JACKSON:   Does your car always make so much racket?
MELVIN:    No, only when it's running.


MR. CLIFFORD:   Dudley, can you tell me what the four seasons are?
DUDLEY:         Salt, pepper, mustard, and vinegar.


MRS. JONES:   What is the highest form of animal life?
JIMMY:        The giraffe.


LESTER:   My cat was on television once.
ROGER:    Really?
LESTER:   Yes. Then my mother chased it off so she could dust the set.


DADDY KANGAROO:   Have you seen our child anywhere, dear?
MAMMA KANGAROO:   Help! Police! I've had my pocket picked.


CUSTOMER:   Who's in charge of this doughnut factory?
WOMAN:      I am—the hole works.


JOHN:   Why do they give girls' names to hurricanes?
ED:     Because they're not "him-icanes."


MARSHALL:   My father has a rabbit tattooed on his arm.
WOODY:      My father has hares all over his chest!


TED:   Last night I did my homework in one hour.
NED:   By the clock?
TED:   No, by the television set.


JOAN:   Never dive into the water on an empty stomach.
JANE:   Why not?
JOAN:   The best way to do it is head first.

ROSS:      I dropped a full glass and didn't spill a bit of water.
RUSSELL:   How did that happen?
ROSS:      It was full of milk.

BEA:       Are you going to take the car out in this rainstorm?
LOU:       Certainly. It's a driving rain, isn't it?

SOPHIE:    Guess I'll be going now. Don't trouble to see me to the door.
SARAH:     It's no trouble, it's a pleasure!

WAITER:    These are the best eggs we've had for years.
LYNDON:    Let's have some you've only had a few days.

MARY:      Oh my goodness, I've been stung by a bee.
HARRY:     Quick, put some ammonia on it.
MARY:      I can't. It flew away.

MRS. LEWIS:   How much is your hamburger steak?
BUTCHER:      Eighty cents a pound.
MRS. LEWIS:   Why, at the corner store it is only fifty cents a pound!
BUTCHER:      Then why don't you buy it there?
MRS. LEWIS:   Because they haven't any.
BUTCHER:      When I don't have it, I sell it for ten cents a pound.

PETER:     How did Jack get that sore jaw?
PAUL:      A girl cracked a smile.
PETER:     Well?
PAUL:      It was *his smile!*

CUSTOMER:  A cup of coffee without cream, please.
WAITER:    I'm sorry. I can't give you coffee without cream because we haven't any cream, but I can give you a cup of coffee without milk.

SY:        I just saw a man jump off a ten-story building.
GUY:       That's nothing—just jump back up—that's the trick!

MR. SMITH:   (To new pupil): Are you the oldest in your family?
NEW PUPIL:   Of course, not. My parents are older.

DRIVER:    I have killed your cat, but I have come to replace it.
MAN:       Very well, but do you think you can catch mice?

TERRY:     Do you know what you get when you cross a duck
           with a cow?
JERRY:     No.  What do you get?
TERRY:     Quackers and milk.

SHORTY:    Did you know that the tallest people are the
           laziest?
STRETCH:   Not true.  Why do you say that?
SHORTY:    Because they are always longer in bed than others.

WALLY:     My father has Lincoln's watch in his collection of
           antiques.
WILLY:     That's nothing.  My father has Adam's apple!

CUSTOMER:  Can I wear this coat in wet weather without
           hurting it?
SALESMAN:  Lady, did you ever see a skunk carrying an
           umbrella?

CAPTAIN:   Why should you never lose your head in battle?
NEW RECRUIT:   Because we would have no place to put our helmets!

NICK:   What did you get the little medal for?
DICK:   For singing.
NICK:   What did you get the big medal for?
DICK:   For stopping.

FATHER:   There's something wrong with my shaving brush.
SON:   That's funny.  It was all right yesterday when I painted my bicycle.

GRACE:   Why does Mr. Moon work as a baker?
TRACY:   I suppose he kneads the dough.

Teacher (Answering the phone): You say Tommy White has a bad cold and can't come to school?  Who is this speaking?
Tommy   (With assumed hoarseness): This is my father.

CLAUDIA:   You remind me of a jet plane.
CLAUDE:   How come?
CLAUDIA:   You're no good on earth.

TEACHER:   Among our spelling words for today is the word "hence." Lenny, can you give me a sentence using the word "hence?"
LENNY:   Hence are female chickens.

The class had been discussing the migration of birds.

TEACHER:   (Holding up a picture of an ostrich): Now, can someone tell me where this bird comes from?
LAURA:   From an egg!

TEACHER:   Birds, though small, are remarkable creatures. For example, what can a little bird do that I cannot do?
CHARLIE:   Take a bath in a saucer.

56

ALAN: Did the people in the audience cry when I died in the second act?

ALICE: Naw, they knew you were only acting.

NEAL: I certainly don't like all these flies.

BUZZ: You just pick out the ones you like and I'll kill all the rest!

BURTON: Will you join me in a bowl of soup?

RUDY: Do you think there's room for both of us?

TEACHER: Can you give me an example of wasted energy?

PEGGY: Yes, sir—telling a hair-raising story to a bald-headed man.

JOSIE: Did your father promise you something if you clean up your room?

ROSIE: No, but he promised me something if I didn't!

TOM: Here comes the parade now. Betty'll miss it if she doesn't come to the window. Where is she?

SUE: She's upstairs waving her hair.

TOM: For heaven's sake, hasn't she got a flag?

MOTHER: Now, Frankie, you must not be selfish. You must let your brother have the sled half the time.

FRANKIE: But, Mother, I do. I have it going down the hill, and he has it coming up.

FLO:      You know Fred Fonzo? He beats his brother every morning.

JOE:      You don't say!

FLO:      Yes. He gets up at seven, and his brother gets up at eight.

RONA:     How do you like cod balls?

MONA:     I don't know. I've never been to one!

TEACHER:  How many fingers have you?

WALLY:    Ten.

TEACHER:  Well, if four were missing, what would you have then?

WALLY:    No music lessons.

SHEILA:   Who's your cook now?

NINA:     Della.

SHEILA:   Della who?

NINA:     Della Katessen!

DOTTY:    Do you think any one can tell the future with cards?

DENNIS:   My mother can. She took one look at my report card and told me exactly what would happen when Dad got home!

MAX:      This soup isn't fit for a pig!

WAITER:   I'll take it back, sir, and bring you some that is!

# Tongue Twisters

Here are 20 ways to dislocate your jaw. Can you say each of
them three times, fast, without getting mixed up?

*Bonnie Bliss blew big bubbles.*
   *A cup of proper coffee in a copper coffee cup.*
    *Katy clattered candy cans.*

*Monday morning mother made mincemeat pies.*
   *Lily ladled little Letty's lentil soup.*
    *I go by a Blue Goose bus.*

*Tim Brook's books.*
   *Sugar sacks should be shaken soundly.*
    *Rush the washing, Russell.*

*His shirt soon shrank in the suds.*
   *The bootblack brought the blank book back.*
    *Bring back some bric-a-brac.*

*Weary Willie's worst weakness was working.*
   *Ted tried to tame tropical tigers.*
    *Tom threw Tim three thumbtacks.*

*Sixty sticky thumbs.*
   *Sally Sanders swept the cinders.*
    *Listen to the local yokel yodel.*

*Buy a black-backed bath brush.*
   *Caesar sighed and seized the scissors.*
    *She was welcoming him in.*

# *Humorous Poems*

## Casey at the Bat

The outlook wasn't brilliant for the Mudville nine that day,
The score stood two to four with just one inning left to play;
And so, when Cooney died at first, and Burrows did the
     same,
A sickly silence fell upon the patrons of the game.

A straggling few got up to go in deep despair. The rest
Clung to the hope that springs eternal within each human
     breast;
They thought if only Casey could but get a whack at that—
They's put up even *money* now, with Casey at the bat.

But Flynn preceded Casey, and so did Jimmy Blake,
And the former was a washout, and the latter was a fake;
So upon that stricken multitude grim melancholy sat,
For there seemed but little chance of Casey's getting to the
     bat.

But Flynn let drive a single to the wonderment of all,
And Blake whom all had sneered at, tore the cover off the
     ball;
And when the dust had lifted, and they saw what had
     occurred,
There was Jimmy safe on second and Flynn a-huggin' third!

Then from the gladdened multitude went up a joyous yell,
It rumbled in the mountaintops, it rattled in the dell,
It struck upon the hillside and rebounded on the flat;
For Casey, mighty Casey, was advancing to the bat.

There was ease in Casey's manner as he stepped into his
    place,
There was pride in Casey's bearing, and a smile on Casey's
    face;
And when, responding to the cheers, he lightly doffed his
    hat,
No stranger in the crowd could doubt 'twas Casey at the
    bat.

Ten thousand eyes were upon him as he rubbed his hands
    with dirt;
Five thousand tongues applauded when he wiped them on
    his shirt.
Then while the writhing pitcher ground the ball into his hip,
Defiance gleamed in Casey's eye, a sneer curled Casey's lip.

And now the leather-covered sphere came hurtling through
    the air,
And Casey stood a-watching it in haughty grandeur there;
Close by the sturdy batsman the ball unheeded sped:
"That ain't my style," said Casey. "Strike one!" the umpire
    said.

From the benches, black with people, there went up a
    muffled roar,
Like the beating of the storm-waves on a stern and distant
    shore;
"Kill him! Kill the umpire!" shouted someone in the stands.
And it's sure they would have killed him had not Casey
    raised his hand.

With a smile of Christian charity great Casey's visage shone;
He stilled the rising tumult; he bade the game go on;
He signaled to the pitcher, and once more the spheroid flew,
But Casey still ignored it; and the umpire said, "Strike two!"

"Fraud!" cried the maddened thousands, and the echo answered "Fraud!"
But one scornful look from Casey and the audience was awed;
They saw his face grow stern and cold, they saw his muscles strain.
And they knew that Casey wouldn't let that ball go by again.

The sneer is gone from Casey's lip, his teeth are clenched with hate;
He pounds with cruel violence his bat upon the plate;
And now the pitcher holds the ball, and now he lets it go.
And now the air is shattered by the force of Casey's blow.

Oh, somewhere in this favored land the sun is shining bright;
The band is playing somewhere, and somewhere hearts are light;
And somewhere men are laughing, and somewhere children shout;
But there is no joy in Mudville—*mighty Casey has struck out!*

*Ernest Lawrence Thayer*

# Casey's Revenge

There were saddened hearts in Mudville for a week or even
    more;
There were muttered oaths and curses—every fan in town
    was sore.
"Just think," said one, "how soft it looked with Casey at the
    bat,
And then to think he'd go and spring a bush league trick like
    that!"

All his past fame was forgotten—he was now a hopeless
    "shine."
They called him "Strike-Out Casey," from the mayor down
    the line;
And as he came to bat each day his bosom heaved a sigh,
While a look of hopeless fury shone in mighty Casey's eye.

He pondered in the days gone by that he had been their
    king,
That when he strolled up to the plate they made the welkin
    ring;
But now his nerve had vanished, for when he heard them
    hoot
He "fanned" or "popped out" daily, like some minor league
    recruit.

He soon began to sulk and loaf, his batting eye went lame;
No home runs on the score card now were chalked against
      his name;
The fans without exception gave the manager no peace,
For one and all kept clamoring for Casey's quick release.

The Mudville squad began to slump, the team was in the air;
Their playing went from bad to worse—nobody seemed to
      care.
"Back to the woods with Casey!" was the cry from Rooters'
      Row.
"Get some one who can hit the ball, and let that big dub
      go!"

The lane is long, some one has said, that never turns again,
And Fate, though fickle, often gives another chance to men;
And Casey smiled; his rugged face no longer wore a frown—
The pitcher who had started all the trouble came to town.

All Mudville had assembled—ten thousand fans had come
To see the twirler who had put big Casey on the bum;
And when he stepped into the box, the multitude went wild;
He doffed his cap in proud disdain, but Casey only smiled.

"Play ball!" the umpire's voice rang out, and then the game
      began.
But in that throng of thousands there was not a single fan
Who thought that Mudville had a chance, and with the
      setting sun
Their hopes sank low—the rival team was leading "four to
      one."

The last half of the ninth came round, with no change in the
score;
But when the first man up hit safe, the crowd began to roar;
The din increased, the echo of ten thousand shouts was
heard
When the pitcher hit the second and gave "four balls" to
the third.

Three men on base—nobody out—three runs to tie the
game!
A triple meant the highest niche in Mudville's hall of fame;
But here the rally ended and the gloom was deep as night,
When the fourth one "fouled to catcher" and the fifth "flew
out to right."

A dismal groan in chorus came; a scowl was on each face
When Casey walked up, bat in hand, and slowly took his
place;
His bloodshot eyes in fury gleamed, his teeth were clenched
in hate;
He gave his cap a vicious hook and pounded on the plate.

But fame is fleeting as the wind and glory fades away;
There were no wild and woolly cheers, no glad acclaim this
day;
They hissed and groaned and hooted as they clamored:
"Strike him out!"
But Casey gave no outward sign that he had heard this
shout.

The pitcher smiled and cut one loose—across the plate it
     sped;
Another hiss, another groan. "Strike one!" the umpire said.
Zip! Like a shot the second curve broke just below the knee.
"Strike two!" the umpire roared aloud; but Casey made no
     plea.
No roasting for the umpire now—his was an easy lot;
But here the pitcher whirled again—was that a rifle shot?
A whack, a crack, and out through the space the leather
     pellet flew,
A blot against the distant sky, a speck against the blue.

Above the fence in center field in rapid whirling flight
The sphere sailed on—the blot grew dim and then was lost
     to sight.
Ten thousand hats were thrown in air, ten thousand threw a
     fit,
But no one ever found the ball that mighty Casey hit.

O, somewhere in this favored land dark clouds may hide the
     sun,
And somewhere bands no longer play and children have no
     fun!
And somewhere over blighted lives there hangs a heavy pall,
But Mudville hearts are happy now, *for Casey hit the ball.*

*Grantland Rice*

# THE OWL AND THE PUSSY-CAT

The Owl and the Pussy-Cat went to sea
    In a beautiful pea-green boat:
They took some honey, and plenty of money
    Wrapped up in a five-pound note.
The Owl looked up to the stars above,
    And sang to a small guitar,
"Oh, lovely Pussy, oh, Pussy, my love,
    What a beautiful Pussy you are,
        You are,
        You are!
What a beautiful Pussy you are!"

Pussy said to the Owl, "You elegant fowl,
    How charmingly sweet you sing!
Oh, let us be married; too long we have tarried:
    But what shall we do for a ring°"

They sailed away for a year and a day,
    To the land where the bong-tree grows;
And there in the wood a Piggy-wig stood,
    With a ring at the end of his nose,
        His nose,
        His nose,
With a ring at the end of his nose.

"Dear Pig, are you willing to sell for one shilling
    Your ring " Said the Piggy, "I will."
So they took it away and were married next day
    By the Turkey who lives on the hill.
They dined on mince and slices of quince,
    Which they ate with a runcible spoon;
And hand in hand, on the edge of the sand,
    They danced by the light of the moon,
        The moon,
        The moon,
They danced by the light of the moon.

*Edward Lear.*

# JABBERWOCKY

'Twas brillig, and the slithy toves
    Did gyre and gimble in the wabe;
All mimsy were the borogoves,
    And the mome raths outgrabe.

"Beware the Jabberwock, my son!
    The jaws that bite, the claws that catch!
Beware the Jubjub bird, and shun
    The frumious Bandersnatch!"

He took his vorpal sword in hand:
    Long time the manxome foe he sought.
So rested he by the Tumtum tree,
    And stood awhile in thought.

And as in uffish thought he stood,
    The Jabberwock with eyes of flame,
Came whiffling through the tulgey wood,
    And burbled as it came!

One, two! One, two! And through, and through
    The vorpal blade went snicker-snack!
He left it dead, and with its head
    He went galumphing back.

"And hast thou slain the Jabberwock?
        Come to my arms, my beamish boy!
Oh, frabjous day!  Callooh! callay!"
        He chortled in his joy.

'Twas brillig, and the slithy toves
        Did gyre and gimble in the wabe;
All mimsy were the borogoves
        And the mome raths outgrabe.

*Lewis Carroll*

# The Stupendous, Titanic Struggle Between Abdul Abulbul Amir and Ivan Skavinsky Skavar

The sons of the Prophet are brave men and bold,
    And quite unaccustomed to fear;
But the bravest by far, in the ranks of the Shah,
    Was Abdul Abulbul Amir.

Now the heroes were plenty and well known to fame,
    In the troops that were led by the Czar,
And the bravest of these was a man by the name
    Of Ivan Skavinsky Skavar.

He could jump fifty yards and tell fortunes at cards,
    And strum on the Spanish guitar,
In fact quite the cream of the Moscovite team
    Was Ivan Skavinsky Skavar.

One day this bold Russian, he shouldered his gun
    And donned his most insolent sneer,
Downtown he did go, where he trod on the toe
    Of Abdul Abulbul Amir.

"Young man," Abdul roared, "with your life are you bored?
    Do you wish to end your career?
Vile infidel, know, you have trod on the toe
    Of Abdul Abulbul Amir!"

"So take your last look at sunshine and brook,
    And send your regrets to the Czar—
For by this I imply, you are going to die,
    Count Ivan Skavinsky Skavar!"

Then this bold Mameluke drew his trusty skibouk,
    Singing "Allah Il Allah! Al-hah"
And with murd'rous intent, he ferociously went,
    For Ivan Skavinsky Skavar.

They parried and thrust, they side-stepped and cussed,
    Of blood they both spilled a great part;
For they both were so tough, so strong and so rough—
    'Twas a wonderful fight from the start!

They fought all that night 'neath the pale yellow moon;
    The din it was heard from afar,
And huge multitudes came, so great was the fame,
    Of Abdul and Ivan Skavar.

As Abdul's long knife was exacting the life,
    In fact, he was shouting "Huzzah!"
He felt himself struck by the wily Calmuck,
    Count Ivan Skavinsky Skavar.

The Sultan drove by in his red-breasted fly,
    Expecting the victor to cheer,
But as he drew nigh he heard the last sigh
    Of Abdul Abulbul Amir.

74

There's a tomb rises up where the Bosporus rolls,
　And carved there in characters clear,
Is, "Stranger, when passing, oh pray for the soul
　Of Abdul Abulbul Amir."

In a Muscovite town 'long the Volga's green banks,
　'Neath the light of the cold Northern Star,
A maid tends the grave of her hero so brave,
　Ivan Skavinsky Skavar!

---

## The Modern Hiawatha

He killed the noble Mudjokivis,
Of the skins he made him mittens,
Made them with the fur side inside,
Made them with the skin side outside.
He, to get the warm side inside,
Put the inside skin side outside;
He, to get the cold side outside,
Put the warm side fur side inside.
That's why he put the fur side inside,
Why he put the skin side outside,
Why he turned them inside outside!

# The Walrus and the Carpenter

The sun was shining on the sea, shining with all his might:
He did his very best to make the billows smooth and
      bright—
And this was odd, because it was the middle of the night.

The moon was shining sulkily, because she thought the sun
Had got no business to be there after the day was done—
"It's very rude of him," she said, "to come and spoil the
      fun!"

The sea was wet as wet could be, the sands were dry as
      dry.
You could not see a cloud, because no cloud was in the sky:
No birds were flying overhead—there were no birds to fly.

The Walrus and the Carpenter were walking close at hand:
They wept like anything to see such quantities of sand.
"If this were only cleared away," they said, "it *would* be
      grand!"

"If seven maids with seven mops swept it for half a year,
Do you suppose," the Walrus said, "that they could get it
      clear?"
"I doubt it," said the Carpenter, and shed a bitter tear.

"O Oysters, come and walk with us!" the Walrus did
    beseech.
"A pleasant walk, a pleasant talk, along the briny beach:
We cannot do with more than four, to give a hand to each."

The eldest Oyster looked at him, but never a word he said:
The eldest Oyster winked his eye, and shook his heavy
    head—
Meaning to say he did not choose to leave the oyster bed.

But four young Oysters hurried up, all eager for the treat:
Their coats were brushed, their faces washed, their shoes
    were clean and neat—
And this was odd, because, you know, they hadn't any feet.

Four other Oysters followed them, and yet another four;
And thick and fast they came at last, and more, and more,
    and more—
All hopping through the frothy waves, and scrambling to the
    shore.

The Walrus and the Carpenter walked on a mile or so,
And then they rested on a rock conveniently low:
And all the little Oysters stood and waited in a row.

"The time has come," the Walrus said, "to talk of many
      things:
Of shoes—and ships—and sealing wax—of cabbages—and
      kings—
And why the sea is boiling hot—and whether pigs have
      wings."

"But wait a bit," the Oysters cried, "before we have our
      chat;
For some of us are out of breath, and all of us are fat!'
"No hurry!" said the Carpenter.  They thanked him much
      for that.

"A loaf of bread," the Walrus said, "is what we chiefly
      need:
Pepper and vinegar besides are very good indeed—
Now, if you're ready, Oysters dear, we can begin to feed."

"But not on us!" the Oysters cried, turning a little blue.
"After such kindness, that would be a dismal thing to do!"
"The night is fine," the Walrus said, "do you admire the
      view?

"It was so kind of you to come.  And you are very nice!"
The Carpenter said nothing but, "Cut us another slice.
I wish you were not quite so deaf—I've had to ask you
      twice!"

"It seems a shame," the Walrus said, "to play them such a
        trick,
After we've brought them out so far, and made them trot so
        quick!"
The Carpenter said nothing but, "The butter's spread too
        thick!"

"I weep for you," the Walrus said, "I deeply sympathize."
With sobs and tears he sorted out those of the largest size,
Holding his pocket-handkerchief before his streaming eyes.

"O Oysters," said the Carpenter, "you've had a pleasant
        run!
Shall we be trotting home again?"  But answer came there
        none—
And this was scarcely odd, because they'd eaten every one.

*Lewis Carroll*

# O'Grady's Goat Done That

O'Grady lived in Shanty Row; but the neighbors often said
They wished that Tim would move away, or that his goat
    were dead
He kept the neighborhood in fear—he was an awful brat;
When trouble came, all said the same:
    *O'Grady's goat done that!*

When e'er there was some devilment, you'd bet your Sunday
    coat,
The neighbors, they would put the blame on Tim O'Grady's
    goat.
On picnic day he tipped the soup and nearly drowned the
    cat,
The ladies gowns were all a mess—
    *O'Grady's goat done that!*

Pat Rooney's wife hung out her wash upon the line to dry;
She went to take it in at night—the neighbors heard a cry:
"The sleeves of those new fancy shirts that I just bought for
    Pat,
They're all chewed off, right to the neck—"
    *O'Grady's goat done that!*

May Flynn was working very hard, the dirty clothes to rub
Upon the washboard, when she dived headfirst into the tub!
She struggled out, she ran around until she found a bat.
"I'll kill the beast who shoved me in!"
    *O'Grady's goat done that!*

Dan Fowler, he brought home a keg of dynamite one day,
To blow a cistern in his yard.  He put the stuff away.
But suddenly an earthquake came—Dan Fowler's house and
    hat
And everything in sight went up—
    *O'Grady's goat done that!*

Mike Doyle was courting Biddy Toole, a pretty little miss.
As they were standing at the gate, all ready for a kiss—
They jammed together like two cars, and mashed their noses
    flat—
Now who broke up *that* romance—Sure!
    *O'Grady's goat done that!*

One winter morning when the snow was deep upon the
    ground,
The folks were sad, yes, very sad—the poor goat dead was
    found!
And in its throat was sticking, as stiff as any bat,
Mag Dolan's missing corset—Yep!
    *O'Grady's goat done that!*

# I Had But Fifty Cents

I took my girl to a fancy ball; we danced till half-past ten,
And when the band stopped playing, for food I got a yen.
So to a restaurant we went, the best one on the street;
She said *she* wasn't hungry, but oh! how she could eat!
A dozen clams, a plate of yams, a chicken and a roast,
Some applesass, asparagrass, and soft-shell crabs on toast,
A big lamb stew, and crackers too—her mouth it was
    immense!
And then some pie—I thought I'd die, *for I had but fifty
    cents.*

Of course, I lost my appetite and didn't care to eat,
Expecting every moment to be kicked into the street;
"Let's see a show," she said to me, "and really have some
    fun!"
—I gave the man my fifty cents, and this is what he done:

He tore my clothes, he smashed my nose,
He hit me on the jaw; he gave me a prize
Of two black eyes, and with me swept the floor!
He took me by the collar, and threw me on the fence;
Take my advice, think more than twice, *if you've got but fifty
    cents.*

# The Yarn of the Nancy Bell

'Twas on the shores that round our coast
    From Deal to Ramsgate span,
That I found alone, on a piece of stone,
    An elderly naval man.

His hair was weedy, his beard was long,
    And weedy and long was he;
And I heard this wight on the shore recite,
    In a singular minor key:—

"Oh, I am a cook and a captain bold,
    And the mate of the Nancy brig,
And a bo'sun tight, and a midshipmite,
    And the crew of the captain's gig."

And he shook his fists and he tore his hair,
    Till I really felt afraid,
For I couldn't help thinking the man had been drinking,
    And so I simply said:—

"Oh, elderly man, it's little I know
    Of the duties of men of the sea,
But I'll eat my hand if I understand
    How ever you can be

"At once a cook and a captain bold,
    And the mate of the Nancy brig,
And a bo'sun tight, and a midshipmite,
    And the crew of the captain's gig!"

Then he gave a hitch to his trousers, which
    Is a trick all seamen larn,
And having got rid of a thumping quid,
    He spun this painful yarn:—

"'Twas in the good ship Nancy Bell
    That we sailed to the Indian sea,
And there on a reef we come to grief,
    Which has often occurred to me.

"And pretty nigh all o' the crew was drowned
    (There was seventy-seven o' soul);
And only ten of the Nancy's men
    Said 'Here!' to the muster-roll.

"There was me, and the cook, and the captain bold,
    And the mate of the Nancy brig,
And the bo'sun tight and a midshipmite,
    And the crew of the captain's gig.

"For a month we'd neither vittles nor drink,
    Till a-hungry we did feel,
So we drawed a lot, and, accordin', shot
    The captain for our meal.

"The next lot fell to the Nancy's mate,
    And a delicate dish he made;
Then our appetite with the midshipmite
    We seven survivors stayed.

"And then we murdered the bo'sun tight,
      And he much resembled pig;
Then we vittled free, did the cook and me,
      On the crew of the captain's gig.

"Then only the cook and me was left,
      And the delicate question, 'Which
   Of us two goes to the kettle?' arose,
   And we argued it out as sich.

"For I loved that cook as a brother, I did,
      And the cook he worshipped me;
But we'd both be blowed if we'd either be stowed
      In the other chap's hold, you see.

"'I'll be eat if you dines off me,' says Tom.
      'Yes, that,'  says I, 'you'll be.
I'm boiled if I die, my friend,' quoth I;
      And 'Exactly so,' quoth he.

"Says he: 'Dear James, to murder me
      Were a foolish thing to do,
For don't you see that you can't cook *me*,
      While I can—and will—cook *you*?'

"So he boils the water, and takes the salt
    And the pepper in portions true,
Which he never forgot, and some chopped shalot,
    And some sage and parsley too.

"'Come here,' says he, with a proper pride,
    Which his smiling features tell;
''Twill soothing be if I let you see
    How extremely nice you'll smell.'

"And he stirred it round and round and round,
    And he sniffed at the foaming froth;
When I ups with his heels, and smothers his squeals
    In the scum of the boiling broth.

"And I eat that cook in a week or less,
    And as I eating be
The last of his chops, why I almost drops,
    For a vessel in sight I see.—

"And I never larf, and I never smile,
    And I never lark nor play;
But sit and croak, and a single joke
    I have—which is to say:

"Oh, I am a cook and a captain bold,
    And the mate of the Nancy brig.
And a bo'sun tight, and a midshipmite,
    And the crew of the captain's gig!"

*W.S. Gilbert*

# The Goat and the Three Red Shirts

There was a man, now please to note,
There was a man, who had a goat;
He lov'd that goat, indeed he did,
He lov'd that goat, just like a kid.

One day that goat felt frisk and fine,
Ate three red shirts from off the line.
The man he grabbed him by the back,
And tied him to a railroad track.

But when the train hove into sight,
That goat grew pale and green with fright.
He heaved a sigh, as if in pain,
Coughed up those shirts and flagged the train!

# You Tell 'Em

You tell 'em, BALDHEAD . . . . *You're smooth!*

You tell 'em, BANK . . . . . . . . *You're safe!*

You tell 'em, BEAN . . . . . . . . *He's stringing you!*

You tell 'em, BUTCHER. . . . . . *You've got lots of tongue!*

You tell 'em, CABBAGE . . . . . *You've got the head!*

You tell 'em, CASHIER . . . . . . *I'm a poor teller!*

You tell 'em, CHLOROFORM . *You put 'em to sleep!*

You tell 'em, CLOCK . . . . . . . . *You've got the time!*

You tell 'em, CRYSTAL . . . . . . *You're on the watch!*

You tell 'em, DENTIST . . . . . . *You've got the pull!*

You tell 'em, DOCTOR . . . . . . *You've got the patience!*

You tell 'em, DOUGH . . . . . . . *You're well-bred!*

You tell 'em, ELECTRICITY . . *You can shock 'em!*

You tell 'em, ENVELOPE. . . . . *You're well posted!*

You tell 'em, GOLDFISH . . . . . *You've been around the globe!*

You tell 'em, HUNTER. . . . . . . *I'm game!*

You tell 'em, JUNE. . . . . . . . . *And don't July!*

You tell 'em, MOUNTAIN . . . . *I'm only a bluff!*

You tell 'em, OPERATOR . . . . *You've got their number!*

You tell 'em, PIE . . . . . . . . . . . *You've got the crust!*

You tell 'em, PRINTER . . . . . . *I'm not your type!*

You tell 'em, RAILROAD. . . . . *It's along your line!*

You tell 'em, SIMON . . . . . . . . *I'll Legree!*

You tell 'em, SKYSCRAPER . . *You've more than one story!*

You tell 'em, TEACHER. . . . . . *You've got the class!*

# Funny Stories

Dan was finishing his report to the class on jet aviation. "Our modern fliers can do anything that a bird can do, and more," he announced proudly.

From a corner of the room, Steve whispered: "I'd like to see one sleeping on a telephone wire with his head tucked under his wing!"

The class was in the middle of its first lesson on baking a cake.

"Mary," said Miss Jones, "please go into the kitchen and see if our cake is done yet. Just stick a knife in the cake and see if it comes out clean."

In a few minutes Mary was back. "Oh, Miss Jones, the knife came out so clean," she said excitedly, "that I stuck in all the other dirty knives too!"

"There's nothing wrong with you," said the shrink to his patient. "Why you're just as sane as I am!"

"But, doctor!" cried the patient, as he brushed wildly at himself, "it's these butterflies. They're all over me!"

"For heaven's sake!" cried the doctor, "don't brush them off on me!"

Lois came home from school and told her mother, "My teacher takes an interest in me. Today she asked me whether I had any younger sisters or brothers, and I told her I am an only child."

"How nice," said her mother, "and what did the teacher say to that?"

"She said, 'Thank goodness.' "

A young lady had just bought a postage stamp.

"Must I stick it on myself?" she asked.

"I should say not," said the post office clerk. "Stick it on the letter."

"Why are these papers strewn all over the place?" asked the sanitation worker.

"Oh," said the supervisor, "those are the leaflets asking people not to throw paper on the ground."

The teacher was speaking to the class.

"Always remember," he said, "that whatever you attempt, there is only one way to learn and that is to begin at the bottom. There are no exceptions to this rule."

A loud whisper from the back of the room asked, "What about swimming?"

As usual, Tony was having trouble with his arithmetic homework. He chewed up three pencils, and sat through two television programs without getting anything on paper. At last he turned to his father. "Pop," he pleaded, "I wish you'd do this arithmetic problem for me."

After thinking a moment, his father said: "You know son, if I did this problem for you, it just wouldn't be right."

"Maybe it wouldn't," said Tony. "But you could try."


"Excuse me," said meek Doug to the big football player in the school cafeteria, "but I think you are sitting on my seat."

"Oh, yeah," growled the football player, "can you prove it?"

"I think so," said Doug. "I left my pie and ice cream on the seat."


It was raining outside and the kindergarten teacher was helping the children of her class in putting on their raincoats, rainhats and rubbers before sending them home. It was an especially hard struggle with little Bobby's galoshes, since they didn't seem to fit too well. She spent more than five minutes getting one of them on Bobby's foot and it was almost as long again before the last buckle snapped into place on the second one.

No sooner had she sighed with relief at the job being over, however, than Bobby said casually, "You know, Mrs. Good, these aren't my galoshes."

"They *aren't?*" With a loud groan of helplessness, the patient teacher turned to the task of removing the galoshes. It took just about as long as putting them on.

"Now, then," said the teacher, "whose galoshes *are* these?"

"They're my brother's," replied Bobby. "He wore them all of last year, before they got too small for him, and now my mother makes *me* wear them!"

The Green children were trying to impress their visiting Uncle Bill. All proudly claimed to be first in something. Bobby said he was first in arithmetic; Susan said she won every spelling bee; James claimed to be best in social studies. Only little Rita was silent.

"Aren't you first in anything, Rita?" asked Uncle Bill.

"Well," Rita replied thoughtfully, "I'm usually the first one out of the class when the bell rings."

In the days of the Old West, a two-gun badman roared into a saloon one day, shooting in all directions. Standing in the middle of the floor, he shouted, "All you dirty bums get out of here!"

In two minutes, the bar was empty, except for one old man, calmly smoking his pipe.

The badman swaggered over to the old man. "Well," he said menacingly.

The old man looked at the bandit calmly. "Sure was a lot of 'em, wasn't there?

As Mark Twain and a friend were coming out of church one morning, it began to pour rain.

"Do you think it will stop?" asked Twain's friend.

The writer looked at the sky. "It always has," he replied.

It had been a trying day for Mrs. Morris, the cooking teacher. The class had been dropping dishes like leaves in the fall. Now Ruth and Dave were cleaning up.

Suddenly there was another loud crash in the pantry.

"More dishes?" asked Mrs. Morris in exasperation.

"No," came a sweet voice from the pantry, "fewer dishes."


A sailor's wife approached the paster of her church just as he was stepping into the pulpit and handed him a note. The note said: "Albert Morse having gone to sea, his wife requests the congregation to pray for his safety."

The minister hastily unfolded the note, and with his mind on the sermon he was about to make, he announced: "Albert Morse, having gone to see his wife, requests the congregation to pray for his safety."


A couple of policeman knocked on the door of the cabin of a hillbilly.

"Say, Bill, Joe and me just found a dead man down by the creek. We came around because we thought it might have been you."

"How big was he?"

"Well, he was about your size—"

"Was he wearing a coonskin cap?"

"Sure enough."

"Was he wearing a blue shirt?"

"Nope!"

"Well, then, it wasn't me."


A man had been out fishing, and was describing to a friend the exact size of the fish he caught.

"It was *so* long," he asserted, spreading his hands far apart. "I never *saw* such a fish."

"Probably not," remarked his friend.

The stutterer met his friend on the street one day.

"J-J-J-Joe," he stammered, "h-h-h-have y-you g-g-got f-f-f-fifteen minutes?"

"Sure," answered his friend. "What is it?"

"I w-w-want t-to have a f-f-f-f-five m-minutes c-c-c-conversation w-with you."


A fisherman, returning home after a day of bad luck, met a friendly old man walking through the woods.

"Have any luck?" asked the old gentleman.

"Nope," replied the fisherman, "but yesterday, before the season opened, I caught 20 bass of all sizes."

"That so?" replied the stranger, "Do you know who I am?"

"Can't say as I do," said the fisherman.

"Well, young man, I'm the game warden!"

"Now isn't that the darndest thing," said the fisherman. "You know who I am? I'm the biggest liar in the United States."


A woman driving in Brooklyn stopped her car for a red light. However, when the light turned green again, she just stayed right where she was.

When the light had changed several times and she still hadn't moved, the traffic policeman finally went over to her and inquired politely, "What's the matter, lady, ain't we got no colors you like?"


Mrs. Nitwit was going out for the day. She locked the house. Then she tacked a note for the grocer on the door:

*"Nobody home. Don't leave anything."*

When she got back that night, she found her door broken open and her house ransacked. On the note she had left, she found the following message added:

*"Thanks! We haven't left much."*

Two little boys had a favor to ask of their mother. They needed her permission for something and were afraid she wouldn't give it to them. "You ask her," said the older one.

"No you."

"Ah, go ahead and ask her," the bigger boy repeated.

"No, it would be better if you did it," answered his younger brother. "You've known her longer than I have."

A farmer was walking down Main Street when he saw a sign over a plumbing supply store. It said *Cast Iron Sinks.*

"Well, by jiminy!" he said. "Anyone knows *that!*"

"Dear Sir," a man wrote to the editor of a country paper. "Can you tell me how long cows should be milked?"

His answer came back in the next mail.

"Just the same as short cows, of course."

A woman was trying to drive her car out of a parking space. First she crashed into the car behind her. Then she bumped into the car in front. Then, pulling out into the street, she smacked right into a delivery truck.

A policeman, who had been watching, came up to her car. "Let's see your license," he demanded.

"Don't be silly, officer," she replied. "Who would give *me* a license?"

A young man just out of school got a job in a bank. The first day he was there, the cashier tossed him a package of bills.

"Here," said the cashier, "count these and see if there are 100."

The young man started counting. He got up to 69, stopped counting, and threw the package into a drawer, saying to the man next to him. "If it's right this far, it's probably right all the way."


President Calvin Coolidge was so famous for his silence that it was considered practically impossible to get him to indulge in any conversation. The story is told that he went to a dinner party and was seated next to a very gushy, high society lady.

"Oh, Mr. President," she said, "do you know, I made a bet today that I could get more than two words out of you!'

"You lose," replied Coolidge.

"Tell me the truth," the sick man told his doctor. "I want to know just how ill I am."

"Well," said the doctor, "you are very sick—very low. In fact, I feel that I should ask you if there is anyone you would like to see."

"Yes," murmured the patient feebly.

"Who is it?"

"Another doctor."